Presented to

RYAN LAMONT

3RD CLASS PRIZE

1995 — 1996

**FEATHERSTONE
METHODIST
CHURCH**

Thy word is a
lamp to my feet and
a light to my path

Psalm 119 v 105

Christian Art, Exeter, 01392 77277

A-FiDDLiNG WE SHALL GO...

Written by Phil McMylor.
Illustrated by Kay Widdowson.

André Deutsch Children's Books

For Pam

Scholastic Children's Books,
Scholastic Publications Ltd,
7-9 Pratt Street, London NW1 0AE

Scholastic Inc.,
730 Broadway, New York, NY 10003, USA

Scholastic Canada Ltd,
123 Newkirk Road, Richmond Hill,
Ontario, Canada L4C 3G5

Ashton Scholastic Pty Ltd,
PO Box 579, Gosford, New South Wales,
Australia

Ashton Scholastic Ltd,
Private Bag 1, Penrose, Auckland,
New Zealand

First published by Scholastic Publications Limited 1993

Text copyright © 1993 by Phil McMylor
Illustrations copyright © 1993 by Kay Widdowson

ISBN: 0 590 54093 9

Printed in Hong Kong by the Paramount Printing Company
Typeset by Rapid Reprographics

10 9 8 7 6 5 4 3 2 1

Old FoxDonald's cupboard was empty. There was nothing for his supper.

So, off he went, over the hills and
across the fields to look for a tasty
bite at a farm he knew well.
He spotted a scarecrow. "I've always
liked hats. Thanks, Mr. Scarecrow,"
he said.

He spied some washing dancing on the line. "That's a jolly coat," he said.

He came across a fiddler fast asleep.
"Ah-ha! A little music always helps a plan along."

"No one will recognise me, now,"
laughed Old FoxDonald.
And he began to play.

He played to the chickens... He played to the cow...

Three sheep, three pigs and a horse
all gathered round to listen.

But not Pip the sheepdog. He just watched.

The geese came along to dance. Even Ginger, the sleepy farmyard cat, woke up and joined the fun.

14

But not Pip the sheepdog. He was still watching.

"Are we all here?" asked Old FoxDonald, with a hungry gleam in his eye.

Fiddling furiously, he led his prancing,
dancing troupe through the gate...

out of the farmyard...   down the lane...

and into the woods.

...FOR SUPPER!

Pip the sheepdog, jumped the gate,

ran straight to the farmhouse door and barked.

Farmer Brown quickly put on his coat...

pulled on his boots...

picked up his gun and...

...raced across the fields to the woods, with Pip leading the way.

Farmer Brown raised his gun, took aim...

...BANG!
Right at Old FoxDonald's bushy tail.

Old FoxDonald ran...down the lane,

across the fields, and over the hills, until he met the fiddler.

"I've lost my fiddle," said the fiddler sadly.

"You can have mine," said Old FoxDonald. "If you let me share your supper."

"Done," said the fiddler. "Do you like bread and cheese?"

So Old FoxDonald, crafty Old FoxDonald got his supper in the end.

And, thanks to Pip the sheepdog, so did all the other animals as well.